INORGANIC REACTIONS
AT ADVANCED LEVEL

**(A student guide for laboratory exercises
in observation and deduction)**

D. G. DAVIES, B.Sc., C.Chem., M.R.I.C.

T. V. G. KELLY, B.Sc.

CollinsEducational

An imprint of HarperCollins*Publishers*

PREFACE

This book is designed to help the student whose examining board has replaced systematic qualitative analysis by simpler, but more interesting, observation and deduction exercises in the practical examination. We have found that it takes a student quite a while to acquire the techniques required to tackle this sort of question well, and it is almost impossible for an 'A' level student to experience at first hand all the reactions which could be encountered, unless other important practical work is to be sacrificed. It is hoped that this book will help to overcome this difficulty. The student should find the book useful throughout his or her 'A' level course but particularly during the early stages. Unfortunately, many part-time students have to attempt 'A' level examinations with limited laboratory experience and these students especially should find the book useful for reference during the practical examination.

A series of observation and deduction exercises has been included and it is hoped that tutors will find this useful. The publishers have kindly agreed to make a key to unknowns available to tutors on request.

We should like to record our thanks to the University of London School Examinations Department for their kind permission to reproduce questions from past examination papers (L). A specimen answer is given, but the Examination Department is in no way responsible for this — it is entirely the work of the authors.

1969   D.G.D.
                                                                                                                      T.K.

The nomenclature of the 1974 edition has been revised to conform to the recommendations for Chemical Nomenclature in G.C.E. Examination Papers, the joint statement recently made by the G.C.E. Boards.

1974   D.G.D.
                                                                                                                      T.K.

Published by Collins Educational
An imprint of HarperCollins*Publishers*
77–85 Fulham Palace Road
Hammersmith
London W6 8JB

© D. G. Davies & T. V. G. Kelly 1969

First published in 1969 by Mills & Boon Limited
Reprinted 1971, 1972, 1974 (revised), 1977, 1979, 1980
Published by Bell & Hyman 1983, reprinted 1984, 1986, 1987
Published by Unwin Hyman 1988, reprinted 1990
Published by CollinsEducational 1991

Reprinted 1992, 1994, 1995, 1997, 1998, 1999, 2000

ISBN 0 00 322230 6

Cover design by Colin S. Lewis & Associates
Printed in Great Britain by Scotprint, Musselburgh

CONTENTS

TABLE 1

COLOURS OF SOLIDS AND SOLUTIONS

A. SOLIDS

COLOUR	SOLID (Bold type indicates that the solid is water-soluble)
Buff	MnS (flesh coloured)
Brown	Ag_2O (greyish); CdO (light); SnS (chocolate); Bi_2S_3 (dark); PbO_2 (dark)
Yellow-brown	**$FeCl_3$ hydrated**
Red-brown	Fe_2O_3; $Fe(OH)_3$; Cu_2O (often red); $Cu_2Fe(CN)_6$
Red	HgO (also yellow form); HgI_2 (yellow above 126^0C); Ag_2CrO_4 (brick red); Cu_2O (sometimes brownish); **$K_3Fe(CN)_6$**; CrO_3
Pink	$CoCO_3$; **hydrated Co^{2+} salts** (very deep colour); **hydrated Mn^{2+} salts** (very pale, often almost white)
Red-orange	Pb_3O_4 (vivid colour); PbO (drab colour)
Orange	Sb_2S_3; SnS_2 (usually yellow); Hg_2CrO_4 (brownish)
Yellow	HgO (muddy) (often red); Bi_2O_3; PbO (often red-orange); HgI_2 (red below 126^0C); CdS; SnS_2 (sometimes orange); PbI_2 (vivid colour); $PbCrO_4$ (vivid colour); $BaCrO_4$ (pale); AgI (pale); AgBr (very pale — cream); **soluble chromates $CrO_4{}^{2-}$**; **$FeCl_3$ hydrated** (brownish); **$K_4Fe(CN)_6$**
Green	Hg_2I_2 (yellowish); $NiCO_3$ (pale); $CuCO_3$ (pale); $Cr_2(CO_3)_3$ (muddy); Cr_2O_3; **hydrated Fe^{2+} salts** (pale); **hydrated Ni^{2+} salts**; **$CuCl_2$ hydrated**; **hydrated Cr^{3+} salts** (sometimes purple); **occasionally $Cu(NO_3)_2$ hydrated**
Blue	**hydrated Cu^{2+} salts**; **anhydrous Co^{2+} salts**
Purple	**Chromium(III) (deep) and iron(III) (pale) alums**
Black	CuO; NiO; CoO; MnO_2; Fe_3O_4; CuS; NiS; CoS; HgS; PbS; Ag_2S; FeS; **$KMnO_4$** (purple lustre)

1

B. SOLUTIONS

COLOUR	ION(S) POSSIBLY PRESENT
Brown	I_3^-, i.e. a soln. of I_2 in I^- (yellow if very dilute); Fe^{3+} (yellowish) (pales on addition of acid)
Orange	$Cr_2O_7^{2-}$ Br_2aq. (soln. bleaches litmus) (yellow if dilute)
Yellow	Fe^{3+} (brownish) (soln. acid to litmus) CrO_4^{2-} (soln. alkaline to litmus) I_3^-, Br_2aq. (see above) (smell of free halogen)
Green	Ni^{2+} (see also under blue) Cr^{3+} (see also under purple) Fe^{2+} (very pale) Cu^{2+} (as a conc. soln. of $CuCl_2$ or, occasionally, of $Cu(NO_3)_2$) MnO_4^{2-} (rare, unless Mn definitely suspected) CrO_2^- (soln. very alkaline to litmus)
Blue	Cu^{2+} Co^{2+} (deep) (conc. soln.) $Cu(NH_3)_4^{2+}$ $Ni(NH_3)_6^{2+}$ } (often deep) (soln. alkaline to litmus, and smell of ammonia)
Purple	MnO_4^- Cr^{3+} (concentrated solution)
Pink	Co^{2+} MnO_4^- (very dil. soln.)

SOLUBILITIES

TABLE II

SOLUBILITIES (in cold water)

In the following table

● = sparingly soluble
O = borderline case
OH⁻ (or other symbol) indicates the nature of the precipitate obtained when the expected compound is unstable or hydrolysed — if a K^+, Na^+ or NH_4^+ salt is used as the source of the anion, e.g. mixing solutions of an Al^{3+} salt and sodium carbonate gives $Al(OH)_3$ and not aluminium carbonate, which is hydrolysed

i.e. $\quad 2Al^{3+} + 3CO_3^{2-} + 3H_2O \rightarrow 2Al(OH)_3 + 3CO_2$

		OH^-	CO_3^{2-}	S^{2-}	Cl^-	Br^-	I^-	NO_3^-	SO_4^{2-}	Other insolubles
Aluminium	Al^{3+}	●	OH^-	OH^-						
Ammonium	NH_4^+									
Antimony	Sb^{3+}	●	OH^-	●						Basic chloride
Barium	Ba^{2+}	O	●	OH^- if conc.					●	CrO_4^{2-}
Bismuth	Bi^{3+}	●	●	●			●			Basic chloride
Cadmium	Cd^{2+}	●	●	●						
Calcium	Ca^{2+}	O	●	OH^- if conc.					O	
Chromium	Cr^{3+}	●	●	OH^-						
Cobalt	Co^{2+}	●	●	●						
Copper	Cu^{2+}	●	●	●						
Iron(III)	Fe^{3+}	●	OH^-	FeS + S						
Iron(II)	Fe^{2+}	●	●	●						
Lead	Pb^{2+}	●	●	●	●	●	●		●	CrO_4^{2-}
Magnesium	Mg^{2+}	●	●	OH^-						
Manganese	Mn^{2+}	●	●	●						
Mercury (II)	Hg^{2+}	HgO	●	●			●			
Mercury (I)	Hg_2^{2+}	HgO + Hg	●	HgS + Hg	●	●	●		●	CrO_4^{2-}
Nickel	Ni^{2+}	●	●	●						
Potassium	K^+									$Co(NO_2)_6^{3-}$
Silver	Ag^+	Ag_2O	●	●	●	●	●		O	CrO_4^{2-}
Sodium	Na^+									
Tin(IV)	Sn^{4+}	●	OH^-	●						
Tin(II)	Sn^{2+}	●	OH^-	●						
Zinc	Zn^{2+}	●	●	●						

TABLE III

THE ACTION OF WATER ON SOLIDS AND SOLUTIONS

If testing a solid, add water, shake, warm if necessary and then cool. Test the solution (or suspension) obtained with litmus paper. (N.B. If a coloured solution is obtained this may mask the colour of the litmus paper. In such a case, after testing, washing the litmus paper with distilled water removes the coloured solution and permits any colour change of the paper to be observed.)

If testing a solution, test first with litmus paper and then add water, dropwise at first, then in large excess.

This table should be used in conjunction with Tables 1 and 11 (Colours and Solubilities).

OBSERVATION	INFERENCE	
	Ion(s) probably present	Probable reaction
1. SOLID DISSOLVES; NO EFFERVESCENCE		
(a) Solution changes litmus paper red → blue	**Solution alkaline, i.e. $[OH^-] > [H^+]$**	
		(i) Solid is an alkali
	$Ca(OH)_2$ $Ba(OH)_2$	only moderately soluble; give suspensions unless water in large excess
		(ii) Solid is a salt of a weak acid and a stronger base, hydrolysed to give an alkaline soln. (Frequently indicates a salt of K^+ or Na^+)
(b) Solution changes litmus paper blue → red	**Solution acid, i.e. $[H^+] > [OH^-]$**	
		(i) Solid is an acid or acid anhydride (rare, unless organic)
		(ii) Solid is an acid salt of a strong acid
	HSO_4^- $H_2PO_4^-$	
		(iii) Solid is a salt of a strong acid and a weaker base, hydrolysed to give an acid soln.
(c) Solution has no effect on litmus paper	**Solution neutral, i.e. $[H^+] = [OH^-]$**	
		Solid is a salt of a strong acid and a strong base and therefore not hydrolysed

2. SOLID DISSOLVES, ACCOMPANIED BY A COLOUR CHANGE	**Probably a change in the degree of hydration of a metal ion** (almost invariably a transition metal)
Test with litmus paper as in 1 above and then refer to Table I	

3. SOLID CAKES AND THEN DISSOLVES SLOWLY	**This usually occurs with anhydrous salts** (or low hydrates) when water is added below the hydrate/anhydrate transition temp. (e.g. Na_2CO_3 with water below about 50^0C)

4. SOLID DISSOLVES ONLY IN HOT WATER AND IS RAPIDLY RE-PRECIPITATED ON COOLING	**Probably a lead(II) halide present**	
(a) White solid → colourless soln.	$PbCl_2$ $PbBr_2$	decreasing solubility in
(b) Yellow solid → colourless soln.	PbI_2	↓ hot water

5. WHITE SOLID DOES NOT DISSOLVE BUT BECOMES OPAQUE AND GIVES A MILKY SUSPENSION	**An insoluble basic salt formed**	
	Sn^{2+}	(usually as $SnCl_2$) basic salt is $Sn(OH)Cl$
	Hg_2^{2+}	($Hg_2(NO_3)_2$ (only soluble salt) formula of basic salt variable
	Bi^{3+}, Sb^{3+}	Soluble salts rarely met; chlorides give basic salts BiOCl and SbOCl

6. SOLID REACTS WITH EFFERVESCENCE		
Colourless gas — evolved, re-lighting a glowing splint	O_2^{2-} (peroxide)	$2O_2^{2-} + 2H_2O \rightarrow 4OH^- + O_2$

7. ACID SOLUTION GIVES WHITE PRE-CIPITATE ON DILUTION WITH WATER; ppt re-dissolves on addition of acid	**Hydrolysis to give an insoluble basic salt**	
	Bi^{3+} Sb^{3+}	e.g. $BiCl_3 + H_2O \rightleftharpoons BiOCl + 2HCl$

TABLE IV

REACTIONS WITH SODIUM HYDROXIDE SOLUTION (or potassium hydroxide)

Add the reagent dropwise to the test solution, observe any changes, then add the reagent in excess. Warm and then boil (taking care if 'bumping' occurs).

OBSERVATION	INFERENCE	
	Ion(s) probably present	Probable reaction
1. PRECIPITATE FORMED; INSOLUBLE IN EXCESS REAGENT	**Insoluble, basic hydroxide or oxide precipitated**	
(a) **White,** turning faintly yellow on heating	Bi^{3+}	$Bi(OH)_3$ pptd; colour change due to partial dehydration
White, rapidly turning pale brown (*N.B. may miss white stage, depending on conditions*)	Mn^{2+}	$Mn(OH)_2$ pptd; aerial oxidation to brown Mn(III) compound
White, no other change	Cd^{2+} or Mg^{2+} (N.B. possibly Ca^{2+}, Ba^{2+} if metal solution is concentrated)	$M(OH)_2$ pptd;
(b) **Brown** (greyish)	Ag^+	Ag_2O pptd (hydroxide unstable)
(c) **Rust-brown**	Fe^{3+}	$Fe(OH)_3$ pptd
(d) **Black**	Hg_2^{2+}	Mixture of HgO and finely divided (black) Hg pptd
(e) **Yellow,** reddening on heating	Hg^{2+}	HgO pptd (hydroxide unstable); colour change due to increase in particle size
(f) **Light-blue,** turning grey-pink on standing, may turn brown; heating accelerates changes	Co^{2+}	Blue basic salt pptd gives pink $Co(OH)_2$ with excess alkali; aerial oxidation to Co(III) compound
(g) **Blue,** turning black on heating	Cu^{2+}	$Cu(OH)_2$ pptd; dehydration to black CuO on heating
(h) **Green**	Ni^{2+}	$Ni(OH)_2$ pptd
(i) **Dark mud-green** (may be initially whitish); turns brown slowly at surface	Fe^{2+}	$Fe(OH)_2$ pptd; aerial oxidation to Fe(III) compound

2. PRECIPITATE FORMED; SOLUBLE IN EXCESS REAGENT	Precipitated hydroxide is amphoteric	
(a) **White** ppt giving a colourless solution (*N.B. tin(II) and tin(IV) ppts are often discoloured*)	Pb^{2+} Zn^{2+} Al^{3+} Sb^{3+} Sn^{2+} Sn^{4+}	$M(OH)_x$ or hydrated oxide pptd; dissolves to give plumbate(II), zincate, aluminate, antimonate(III), stannate(II), stannate(IV) respectively.
(b) **Grey-green** ppt giving dark green solution (*N.B. if original solution is too dilute ppt may not appear*)	Cr^{3+}	$Cr(OH)_3$ pptd, dissolves to give chromite
3. SOLUTION CHANGES COLOUR ORANGE → YELLOW	$Cr_2O_7^{2-}$	Dichromate converted to chromate $Cr_2O_7^{2-} + 2OH^- \rightarrow 2CrO_4^{2-} + H_2O$
4. AMMONIA EVOLVED, either when cold or on warming	NH_4^+	$NH_4^+ + OH^- \rightarrow NH_3 + H_2O$
(a) **No other change**	NH_4^+ alone as cation or with Na^+, K^+	
(b) **And a precipitate formed** (*N.B. usually indicates a double salt*)	NH_4^+ and see 1 and 2 above	
(c) **And solution changes colour orange → yellow**	NH_4^+ and $Cr_2O_7^{2-}$ together	Soln. of ammonium dichromate converted to soln. of sodium chromate, and ammonia liberated
5. NO APPARENT CHANGE	(a) Na^+, K^+ (N.B. possibly Ca^{2+}, Ba^{2+} if metal solution is dilute)	
	(b) No metals present	Possibly a solution of an acid or H_2O_2

TABLE V

REACTIONS WITH AMMONIA SOLUTION

Add the reagent to the test solution, observe any changes, then add the reagent in excess. Warm and then boil (taking care if 'bumping' occurs). **Read note at end of table.**

OBSERVATION	INFERENCE	
	Ion(s) probably present	Probable reaction
1. PRECIPITATE FORMED; INSOLUBLE IN EXCESS REAGENT	**Insoluble hydroxide or basic salt pptd; no complex ions of type $M(NH_3)_x^{n+}$ formed**	
(a) **White**	Bi^{3+}	Basic salt pptd
	Pb^{2+}, Al^{3+} Mg^{2+}, Sb^{3+} Sn^{2+}, Sn^{4+}	Hydroxide or hydrated oxide pptd
	Hg^{2+}	Mercury(II) aminochloride, $Hg(NH_2)Cl$, pptd
(b) **Brownish-white** (*N.B. may be white initially but soon darkens*)	Mn^{2+}	$Mn(OH)_2$ pptd; aerial oxidation to brown Mn(III) compound
(c) **Rust-brown**	Fe^{3+}	$Fe(OH)_3$ pptd
(d) **Grey-green**	Cr^{3+}	$Cr(OH)_3$ pptd
(e) **Mud-green** (may be initially whitish) darkening to grey on heating; slowly turns brown at surface	Fe^{2+}	$Fe(OH)_2$ pptd; aerial oxidation to brown Fe(III) compound
(f) **Black**	Hg_2^{2+}	Mixture of $Hg(NH_2)Cl$ and finely divided (black) Hg pptd
(g) **Dirty-blue**, darkening with excess reagent (*N.B. ppt may dissolve in excess reagent if this is fairly concentrated, to give a yellow-brown solution*)	Co^{2+}	Basic salt pptd
2. PRECIPITATE FORMED; SOLUBLE IN EXCESS REAGENT	**Insoluble oxide or hydroxide pptd, dissolving in excess reagent by complex ion formation**	
(a) **White** ppt → colourless solution	Cd^{2+}, Zn^{2+}	$M(OH)_2$ pptd, then giving $M(NH_3)_4^{2+}$

NH$_3$(aq)

(b) **Blue** ppt → very deep blue solution	Cu^{2+}	Ditto
(c) **Green** ppt → deep blue solution. (*N.B. this ppt is often transient and difficult to observe unless Ni^{2+} solution is concentrated*)	Ni^{2+}	Ni(OH)$_2$ pptd, then giving Ni(NH$_3$)$_6$$^{2+}$
(d) **Brown** ppt → colourless solution (*N.B. This ppt is often transient*)	Ag$^+$	Ag$_2$O pptd (hydroxide unstable) then giving Ag(NH$_3$)$_2$$^+$
(e) **Dirty blue** ppt (see 1(g) above)	Co^{2+}	
3. SOLUTION CHANGES COLOUR ORANGE → YELLOW	Cr$_2$O$_7$$^{2-}$	Dichromate converted to chromate $$Cr_2O_7{}^{2-} + 2OH^- \rightarrow 2CrO_4{}^{2-} + H_2O$$
4. NO APPARENT CHANGE (though possibly a slight turbidity of CaCO$_3$ or BaCO$_3$ due to presence of CO$_3$$^{2-}$ ions in ammonia solution)	(a) Na$^+$, K$^+$ Ca^{2+}, Ba^{2+} NH$_4$$^+$	Hydroxide soluble
	(b) No metals present	Possibly a solution of an acid or H$_2$O$_2$

NOTE: Hydroxides of the following have relatively high solubility products and are not precipitated by ammonia solution in the presence of ammonium salts (i.e. NH$_4$$^+$ ions):

$$Zn^{2+}, \quad Mg^{2+}, \quad Co^{2+}, \quad Ni^{2+}, \quad Mn^{2+}$$

TABLE VI

REACTIONS WITH DILUTE HYDROCHLORIC ACID

Add a little of the acid to the test solution (or solid, if this is to be used) — observe in the cold, testing for gases if necessary — then warm and observe again. Add an excess of the acid if this is necessary to dissolve any solid used. (*N.B. Great care must be taken to distinguish between the spray or vapours of the hydrochloric acid (particularly if warm) and any gases or other vapours produced by the reaction.*)

OBSERVATION	INFERENCE	
	Ion(s) probably present	Probable reaction
1. GAS OR VAPOUR EVOLVED	**Salt of a weak acid present, the acid being either unstable or volatile; or metal above H in E.C.S.**	
A. **Colourless**		
(a) *odourless* and turning lime-water milky	CO_3^{2-}, HCO_3^-	CO_2 evolved by either of reactions: $CO_3^{2-} + 2H^+ \rightarrow CO_2 + H_2O$ $HCO_3^- + H^+ \rightarrow CO_2 + H_2O$
(b) *odourless*, burning with a blue flame if sufficient present (often mildly explosive)	Free metal above H in E.C.S.	Hydrogen displaced, e.g. $M + 2H^+ \rightarrow M^{2+} + H_2$
(c) *odourless*, relighting a glowing splint (reaction normally only with solid)	O_2^{2-} (peroxide)	H_2O_2 formed, some decomposing to give oxygen
(d) *rotten egg smell*, turning damp lead (II) ethanoate (acetate) paper black	S^{2-}, HS^-	H_2S liberated by either of reactions: $S^{2-} + 2H^+ \rightarrow H_2S$ $HS^- + H^+ \rightarrow H_2S$
(e) *vinegar smell* (usually requires warming)	CH_3COO^-	Ethanoic (acetic) acid displaced $CH_3COO^- + H^+ \rightarrow CH_3COOH$
(f) *very pungent* (may require warming), turning damp dichromate paper green		SO_2 liberated, reducing $Cr_2O_7^{2-}$ to Cr^{3+}
(i) no accompanying ppt	SO_3^{2-}	$SO_3^{2-} + 2H^+ \rightarrow SO_2 + H_2O$
(ii) accompanying fine ppt of sulphur (white to yellow)	$S_2O_3^{2-}$	$S_2O_3^{2-} + 2H^+ \rightarrow S + SO_2 + H_2O$

B. **Pale green**, pungent, bleaching damp litmus paper. Solution turns pale greenish-yellow	OCl^-	Cl_2 liberated $OCl^- + 2H^+ + Cl^- \rightarrow Cl_2 + H_2O$
C. **Brown**, pungent. Solution often turns pale blue	NO_2^-	Unstable nitrous acid displaced $H^+ + NO_2^- \rightarrow HNO_2$ decomposing to give oxides of nitrogen
2. NO GAS OR VAPOUR EVOLVED BUT WATER-INSOLUBLE SOLID DISSOLVES IN ACID (only applicable when test made on solid)	**Metal oxide or hydroxide present or salt of a weak acid, the acid being stable and involatile; Pb^{2+}, Hg_2^{2+}, Ag^+ are absent**	
	OH^-, PO_4^{3-}, $C_2O_4^{2-}$, CrO_4^{2-}	Hydroxyl ions or acid anions react with H^+ $H^+ + B^- \rightarrow HB$
3. COLOUR OF SOLUTION CHANGES YELLOW → ORANGE	CrO_4^{2-}	Chromate converted to dichromate $2CrO_4^{2-} + 2H^+ \rightarrow Cr_2O_7^{2-} + H_2O$
4. WHITE PRECIPITATE (OR RESIDUE IF REACTION PERFORMED ON SOLID) (*N.B. see also $S_2O_3^{2-}$ above*)	**Metal chloride is insoluble**	
(a) Insoluble on boiling but dissolving on addition of excess ammonia	Ag^+	Complex $Ag(NH_3)_2^+$ formed
(b) Insoluble on boiling but turning black on addition of excess ammonia	Hg_2^{2+}	Mixture of $Hg(NH_2)Cl$ and finely divided (black) Hg formed
(c) Soluble (usually) on boiling; re-pptd on cooling. Ammonia has little apparent effect (may cause extra cloudiness)	Pb^{2+}	$PbCl_2$ considerably more soluble in hot water than in cold.

H_2SO_4
(dil.)
(see p.12)

TABLE VIA

REACTIONS WITH DILUTE SULPHURIC ACID

This reagent gives similar reactions to dilute hydrochloric acid (TABLE VI) in sections 1 and 3. Sections 2 and 4, however, differ. The same general procedural instructions apply.

OBSERVATION	INFERENCE	
	Ion(s) probably present	Probable reaction
2. NO GAS OR VAPOUR EVOLVED BUT WATER-INSOLUBLE SOLID DISSOLVES IN ACID (only applicable when test made on solid)	Metal oxide or hydroxide present or salt of a weak acid, the acid being stable and involatile. Pb^{2+}, Hg_2^{2+}, Ca^{2+}, Ba^{2+} (and exceptionally Ag^+) are absent	
	OH^-, PO_4^{3-} $C_2O_4^{2-}$, CrO_4^{2-}	Hydroxyl ions or acid anions react with H^+ $H^+ + B^- \to HB$
4. WHITE PRECIPITATE (OR RESIDUE IF REACTION PERFORMED ON SOLID) (*N.B. see also* $S_2O_3^{2-}$ *above*)	Pb^{2+}, Hg_2^{2+} Ca^{2+}, Ba^{2+} (exceptionally Ag^+ if Ag^+ soln. is concentrated)	Sulphate pptd $M^{2+} + SO_4^{2-} \to MSO_4$

TO DISTINGUISH BETWEEN Pb^{2+}, Hg_2^{2+}, Ca^{2+}, Ba^{2+}, (Ag^+)

To a little of the test solution add potassium chromate solution. If only solid is available this should be dissolved in the minimum quantity of dilute nitric acid and then diluted two or three times.

1. Yellow ppt, intensely coloured	Pb^{2+}	
2. Yellow ppt, pale	Ba^{2+}	
3. Brownish-orange ppt	Hg_2^{2+}	Chromate pptd
4. Red ppt	Ag^+	
5. No ppt	Ca^{2+}	

TABLE VII

REACTIONS WITH SODIUM CARBONATE SOLUTION

Add the reagent dropwise to the test solution, observe any change, then add the reagent in excess. Warm and then boil (taking care if bumping occurs).

N.B. The majority of carbonates precipitated by this reagent are basic carbonates (see Revision Notes for Advanced Level Inorganic Chemistry, Ch. 3, publ. Allman) and the student should appreciate that formulae used in the following table are simplified.

OBSERVATION	INFERENCE	
	Ion(s) probably present	Probable reaction
1. PRECIPITATE FORMED	**Insoluble carbonate, hydroxide or oxide precipitated**	
(a) **White**, no other change (*N.B. Solutions containing Bi^{3+} are always very acid and some effervescence (CO_2) may precede precipitation*)	Pb^{2+}, Bi^{3+}, Cd^{2+}, Zn^{2+}, Ca^{2+}, Ba^{2+}, Mg^{2+}	Metal carbonate precipitated
White, accompanied by effervescence (*N.B. Observation with Sn^{2+}, Sn^{4+} and Sb^{3+} is difficult because the same conditions apply as with Bi^{3+}, above*)	Al^{3+}, Sn^{2+} Sn^{4+}, Sb^{3+}	Hydroxide precipitated; carbonate unstable, hence CO_2 evolved
White, rapidly turning pale brown (*N.B. may miss white stage, depending on conditions*)	Mn^{2+}	$MnCO_3$ pptd; aerial oxidation to brown Mn(III) compound
White, darkening on heating	Ag^+	Ag_2CO_3 pptd; some decomposition to Ag_2O on heating
(b) **Cream**, darkening on heating	Hg_2^{2+}	Hg_2CO_3 pptd; then decomposition to HgO and Hg on heating
(c) **Yellow (ochre) immediately turning brown**, then yellow-orange on heating	Hg^{2+}	$HgCO_3$ pptd; colour changes due to decomposition to HgO
(d) **Light blue**, darkening on heating and turning black	Cu^{2+}	$CuCO_3$ pptd; decomposition to black CuO
(e) **Red brown**, accompanied by effervescence (*N.B. not gelatinous as when reagent is NaOH or NH_3(aq)*)	Fe^{3+}	$Fe(OH)_3$ pptd; carbonate unstable, hence CO_2 evolved

(f) **Mud-green** (*N.B. With Fe²⁺ the ppt may pass through an initial whitish stage; it also darkens at the surface on standing*)	Fe^{2+}, Cr^{3+}	Carbonates pptd
(g) **Light green**	Ni^{2+}	$NiCO_3$ pptd
(h) **Mauve**, becoming blue on heating	Co^{2+}	$CoCO_3$ pptd
2. **AMMONIA EVOLVED**, either when cold or on gentle warming	NH_4^+	Sodium carbonate hydrolysed to give an alkaline soln. which displaces weak base $$CO_3^{2-} + 2H_2O \rightleftharpoons H_2CO_3 + 2OH^-$$ $$NH_4^+ + OH^- \rightarrow NH_3 + H_2O$$

(**N.B. Evolution of ammonia may accompany precipitation of a carbonate or hydroxide.** If this occurs it indicates the presence of both NH_4^+ and another cation — possibly originating from a double salt. The precipitate may be identified as in 1, above)

3. **EFFERVESCENCE, COLOURLESS GAS EVOLVED**, turning lime-water milky. No other change	**Acid present, or acid salt of strong acid, e.g. HSO_4^- ions**	$$CO_3^{2-} + 2H^+ \rightarrow CO_2 + H_2O$$
4. **COLOUR OF SOLUTION CHANGES ORANGE → YELLOW**, together with slight effervescence	$Cr_2O_7^{2-}$	Alkaline soln. from hydrolysis of Na_2CO_3 effects change $$Cr_2O_7^{2-} + 2OH^- \rightarrow 2CrO_4^{2-} + H_2O$$
5. **NO APPARENT CHANGE**	K^+, Na^+ H_2O_2	

TABLE VIII

H_2SO_4
(conc.)

REACTIONS OF SOLIDS WITH CONCENTRATED SULPHURIC ACID

N.B. If it is suspected that a permanganate or chlorate(V) is present then on no account must this reagent be used. Reactions of concentrated sulphuric acid with these compounds can be violently explosive.

Reactions of this reagent with salts of weak acids (CO_3^{2-}, SO_3^{2-}, CH_3COO^-, etc.) are as for dil.HCl and dil. H_2SO_4, but they are usually more vigorous. An exception occurs with sulphides (see table below).

Add the reagent dropwise initially and then in excess (normally not more than about 3 cm^3). Warm **gently** — overheating will cause thermal decomposition of the reagent, giving white fumes of SO_3. After observation **allow the test-tube to cool** before disposal of the contents into a sink of running water. **Pouring hot, concentrated sulphuric acid into water can be extremely dangerous.**

The observation of fuming gases and vapours such as HCl, HBr, HI, CrO_2Cl_2, is facilitated by blowing across the mouth of the test-tube.

OBSERVATION	INFERENCE	
	Ion(s) probably present	Probable reaction
(a) **Colourless, pungent gas, fuming heavily in air** (frothy effervescence)	Cl^-	Volatile HCl displaced $Cl^- + H_2SO_4 \rightarrow HCl + HSO_4^-$
(b) **Colourless acid vapours, becoming pale brown on moderate heating.** Slight fuming in air; liquid often pale yellow; colourless liquid may be observed condensing and running back	NO_3^-	Volatile HNO_3 displaced $NO_3^- + H_2SO_4 \rightarrow HNO_3 + HSO_4^-$ Some thermal decomposition $4HNO_3 \rightarrow 2H_2O + 4NO_2 + O_2$
(c) **Red-brown vapours, pungent, fuming heavily in air.** Frothy effervescence. Red-brown liquid condenses and runs back	Br^-	Volatile HBr displaced $Br^- + H_2SO_4 \rightarrow HBr + HSO_4^-$ Some oxidation to bromine
(d) **Frothy effervescence, red-brown vapours on warming.** Red, oily droplets in liquid — also condensing and running back. Heavy fuming in air	$Cr_2O_7^{2-}$ and Cl^- (orange) or CrO_4^{2-} and Cl^- (yellow)	CrO_2Cl_2 formed (also much HCl)

N.B. To distinguish between NO_2, Br_2, CrO_2Cl_2, see Table XV, p. 31

(e) **Black solid pptd, colourless pungent gas evolved, fuming heavily in air. Violet vapours observed on heating**	I^-	Oxidation to iodine; HI also evolved. Purple is iodine vapour

(f) **Yellow solid turns bright red.** Much heat evolved	CrO_4^{2-}	Chromic acid displaced Chromium(VI) oxide formed $CrO_4^{2-} + 2H_2SO_4 \rightarrow$ $2HSO_4^- + H_2O + CrO_3$
(g) **Orange solid turns bright red.** Much heat evolved	$Cr_2O_7^{2-}$	$Cr_2O_7^{2-} + 2H_2SO_4 \rightarrow$ $2HSO_4^- + H_2O + 2CrO_3$
(h) **Dark brown solid yields oxygen,** and eventually leaves white residue. Heat essential	Oxide PbO_2	Change of oxidation state, lead (IV) oxide → lead (II) sulphate
(i) **Orange-red solid yields oxygen,** and eventually leaves white residue. Heat essential	Oxide Pb_3O_4	Ditto; lead (II,IV) oxide → lead (II) sulphate
(j) **Black solid yields oxygen** and eventually leaves a whitish residue. Heat essential	Oxide MnO_2	Ditto; manganese (IV) oxide → manganese (II) sulphate
(k) **Yellow-white residue formed; hydrogen sulphide evolved**	S^{2-}	Displacement of weak acid H_2S, some oxidation to sulphur
(l) **Red or pink solid turns blue**	Co^{2+}	Formation of anhydrous sulphate from a hydrated salt: $Cu(H_2O)_4^{2+} \rightarrow Cu^{2+} + 4H_2O$
(m) **Blue solid turns white**	Cu^{2+}	Many other examples
(n) **Pungent sulphur dioxide evolved**	**Reducing agent** present (N.B. not all reducing agents give this reaction)	

TABLE IX

REACTIONS WITH HYDROGEN SULPHIDE

Since hydrogen sulphide is a weak acid, electrolyte and the solubility products of sparingly soluble sulphides vary widely, reactions of the reagent are dependent on the pH's of the solutions being treated. As a rough guide, the student should apply the following criteria in deciding whether a solution is acid, 'neutral' or alkaline:

Acid solutions may be taken as those which are prepared by dissolving a solid in a dilute acid, or aqueous solutions to which acid has subsequently been added.

'Neutral' solutions may be taken as those which are prepared by dissolving a solid in distilled water.

Alkaline solutions are usually encountered under one of the following conditions:

(i) A precipitated amphoteric oxide or hydroxide has been dissolved in excess caustic alkali.

(ii) A precipitated hydroxide has been dissolved in excess aqueous ammonia by complex ion formation.

(iii) A solution has been treated with ammonium chloride (or other ammonium salt) and then aqueous ammonia without resulting in hydroxide precipitation (i.e. any metals present have hydroxides with comparatively high solubility products).

N.B. (a) Most 'neutral' solutions as described above will give an acid or alkaline reaction with litmus. This is due to salt hydrolysis and may usually be ignored.

(b) If provided with a ready prepared solution for analysis, the student should use the litmus test as a guide. A weakly acid or alkaline reaction should be taken as indicating a 'neutral' solution.

Pass H_2S through a little of the test solution at slow to moderate rate. Some precipitates are often slow to appear and others may change their appearance as more H_2S is passed; the gas should, therefore, be bubbled for not less than 20 – 30 seconds.

OBSERVATION	INFERENCE	
	Ion(s) probably present	Probable reaction
1. NO PRECIPITATE	Metal sulphide is soluble in water, is completely hydrolysed or is sparingly soluble and has a relatively high solubility product; or no metal ions present	
(N.B. Solutions of Co^{2+}, Ni^{2+}, Fe^{2+} may darken slightly after passing H_2S, particularly if heated — possibly a sulphide sol is formed. An Fe^{2+} sample which has undergone sufficient aerial oxidation to Fe^{3+} may yield a faint white mistiness of S)	NH_4^+, K^+, Na^+, Ba^{2+}, Ca^{2+}, Mg^{2+}, Al^{3+}, Cr^{3+}, Mn^{2+}, Co^{2+}, Ni^{2+}, Fe^{2+}, H_2O_2	
2. PRECIPITATE FORMED	Metal sulphide is sparingly soluble in water and has a relatively low solubility product; OR An oxidising agent is present oxidising H_2S to S	
(i) *A colourless solution giving*		
(a) **black** ppt	Pb^{2+}, Hg_2^{2+}, Ag^+	PbS, Hg + HgS, Ag_2S pptd
(b) **dark brown** ppt	Bi^{3+}, Sn^{2+}	Bi_2S_3, SnS pptd
(c) **yellow** ppt	Cd^{2+}, Sn^{4+}	CdS, SnS_2 pptd
(d) **orange** ppt	Sb^{3+}	Sb_2S_3 pptd
(e) **yellow-brown** ppt turning rapidly **black**	Hg^{2+}	Double salts (e.g. $HgCl_2$, HgS) first pptd, then converted to HgS
(f) **white** (fine) ppt	Zn^{2+}	ZnS pptd
(ii) *A yellow or orange solution giving*		
(a) **white to yellow** (fine) ppt	Fe^{3+}	H_2S oxidised to S and Fe^{3+} reduced to Fe^{2+}

OBSERVATION	Ion(s) probably present	Probable reaction
(b) **muddy green** suspension from yellow solution	CrO_4^{2-}	H_2S oxidised to S, and green Cr^{3+} ions formed by reduction
(c) **muddy green** suspension from orange solution	$Cr_2O_7^{2-}$	
(iv) A *blue or green solution giving* **black** ppt	Cu^{2+}	CuS pptd
(v) A *purple solution giving* **dirty white** (fine) ppt and purple colour dispersed	MnO_4^-	H_2S oxidised to S, and MnO_4^- ions reduced to Mn^{2+}

B. FOR ACID SOLUTIONS

Observations are essentially as for 'neutral' solutions. The following are important exceptions:
1. Zn^{2+} is not pptd from acid solutions.
2. Cd^{2+} will not be pptd as CdS from strongly acid solutions because the solubility product of the latter is not exceeded. If cadmium is suspected to be present in an acid solution and a test is to be made with H_2S, a portion of the solution should be diluted about 5 times before passing the gas.

C. FOR ALKALINE SOLUTIONS

OBSERVATION	INFERENCE	
	Ion(s) probably present	Probable reaction
1. NO PRECIPITATE	Metal sulphide is soluble in water or is completely hydrolysed	
	NH_4^+, K^+, Na^+, Ba^{2+}, Ca^{2+}, Mg^{2+}, Al^{3+}, Cr^{3+}	
2. PRECIPITATE FORMED	Metal sulphide is sparingly soluble in water	
(i) A *colourless solution giving*		
(a) **black** ppt	Pb^{2+}, Ag^+	PbS, Ag_2S pptd; if PbS then Pb present as plumbate(II) (PbO_2^{2-}); if Ag_2S then Ag present as $Ag(NH_3)_2^+$

(b) **dark brown** ppt	Sn^{2+}	SnS pptd; Sn present as stannate(II) (SnO_2^{2-})
(c) **yellow** ppt	Cd^{2+}	CdS pptd; Cd present as $Cd(NH_3)_4^{2+}$
(d) **white** ppt	Zn^{2+}	ZnS pptd; Zn present as ZnO_2^{2-} or $Zn(NH_3)_4^{2+}$
(e) **buff** (or **flesh coloured**) ppt	Mn^{2+}	MnS pptd
(ii) *A blue solution giving*		
black ppt	Ni^{2+}, Cu^{2+}	NiS, CuS pptd; if NiS then Ni present as $Ni(NH_3)_6^{2+}$; if CuS then Cu present as $Cu(NH_3)_4^{2+}$
(iii) *A pink to gold solution giving* (N.B. the colour here depends on the concentration of ammonia)		
black ppt	Co^{2+}	CoS pptd; Co present either as Co^{2+} (pink) or $Co(NH_3)_4^{2+}$ (gold) depending on the ammonia concentration

TABLE X

REACTIONS WITH SILVER NITRATE SOLUTION

Add the reagent dropwise to the test solution, observe, then add excess and warm.

OBSERVATION	INFERENCE	
	Ion(s) probably present	Probable reaction
1. PRECIPITATE FORMED		
(a) **White**, curdy, turning buff on heating	CO_3^{2-}, HCO_3^-	Hg_2CO_3 pptd
White, curdy, turning purplish grey on standing in bright light; insoluble in dil. HNO_3	Cl^-	AgCl pptd
(b) **Cream** (pale, sometimes almost white)	Br^-	AgBr pptd
Cream (deep, sometimes almost yellow) (*N.B. Ag$_3$PO$_4$ is soluble in both NH$_3$(aq) soln. and in dil. HNO$_3$; AgI is insoluble in these reagents*)	PO_4^{3-}, I^-	Ag_3PO_4, AgI pptd respectively
(c) **Red** from yellow soln. from orange soln.	CrO_4^{2-} $Cr_2O_7^{2-}$	Ag_2CrO_4 pptd
(d) **Greyish-brown** (*N.B. If NH$_3$(aq) soln. is used the initial ppt is transient – dissolving in the excess NH$_3$(aq) forming complex ion Ag(NH$_3$)$_2$$^+$*)	OH^-	Ag_2O pptd (AgOH unstable)
(e) **Black** (*N.B. If Ag is pptd this is sometimes brownish and sometimes in the form of a mirror*)	S^{2-} Fe^{2+} SnO_2^{2-}	Ag_2S pptd Ag pptd in redox reactions $Fe^{2+} + Ag^+ \rightleftharpoons Ag + Fe^{3+}$ $SnO_2^{2-} + 2OH^- + 2Ag^+ \rightleftharpoons$ $SnO_3^{2-} + 2Ag + H_2O$
2. CRYSTALLINE GROWTH OF SILVER SLOWLY FORMED	Redox reaction of displacement type by metal above Ag in E.C.S. e.g. $$Cu + 2Ag^+ \rightarrow Cu^{2+} + 2Ag$$	
3. NO APPARENT REACTION	No anion present which can give insoluble silver salt by double decomposition. Reducing agents such as Fe^{2+}, SnO_2^{2-}, SO_3^{2-} absent	

TABLE XI

SOME IMPORTANT REACTIONS OF POTASSIUM CHROMATE (AND POTASSIUM DICHROMATE)

The chromate and dichromate ions are related:

$$2CrO_4^{2-} + 2H^+ \rightleftharpoons Cr_2O_7^{2-} + H_2O$$

chromate	dichromate
(yellow)	(orange)

In the following table an aqueous solution of the reagent is used unless otherwise stated.

Add a few drops of the reagent to the test solution, observe any changes, and then warm.

OBSERVATION	INFERENCE	
	Ion(s) probably present	Probable reaction
1. PRECIPITATE FORMED	Insoluble chromate precipitated	
(a) **Pale yellow** (insoluble in NaOH aq.)	Ba^{2+}	$BaCrO_4$ pptd
(b) **Canary yellow**, becoming orange on heating (yellow ppt is soluble in NaOH aq.)	Pb^{2+}	$PbCrO_4$ pptd
(c) **Brick red**	Ag^+	Ag_2CrO_4 pptd
(d) **Orange-brown**	Hg_2^{2+}	Hg_2CrO_4 pptd
(N.B. *The majority of stable chromates are insoluble, but those given above are the examples commonly encountered.*)		
2. SOLUTION (CHROMATE) CHANGES YELLOW → ORANGE	Solution being tested is acidic (see equation at beginning of table) (a) Solution contains added acid (b) Salt present is hydrolysed to give an acid solution	
3. SOLUTION (DICHROMATE) CHANGES ORANGE → YELLOW	Solution being tested is alkaline H^+ ions removed, $H^+ + OH^- \rightarrow H_2O$ and equilibrium (see beginning of table) moves to left (a) Solution contains added alkali (b) Salt present is hydrolysed to give an alkaline solution	

4. SOLUTION CHANGES YELLOW (CHROMATE) → GREEN, or ORANGE (DICHROMATE) → GREEN	**Reducing agent present in acid solution** Chromium is reduced from Cr(VI) state to Cr(III) state e.g. $Cr_2O_7^{2-} + 14H^+ + 6e \rightarrow 2Cr^{3+} + 7H_2O$

(N.B. If the reducing agent is I^- iodine is liberated in the presence of acid and the dark brown colour of iodine will mask the green of Cr^{3+} ions. Solid I_2 may be pptd.)

5. SOLUTION CHANGES ORANGE (OR YELLOW) → BLUE → GREEN and effervescence occurs	H_2O_2 in presence of H^+ ions	Blue CrO_5 formed; decomposes to give green Cr^{3+} soln.; O_2 evolved

Important reactions of solid potassium dichromate (or chromate) are dealt with in

Table VIII (d), (f) and (g)

Table XVIII, chloride (d)

TABLE XII

REACTIONS WITH POTASSIUM IODIDE SOLUTION

Add the reagent dropwise initially and then add excess. Warm. If there is no apparent reaction on adding the reagent add a little dilute sulphuric acid.

OBSERVATION	INFERENCE	
	Ion(s) probably present	Probable reaction
1. PRECIPITATE FORMED, INSOLUBLE IN EXCESS REAGENT	**Sparingly soluble iodide pptd; no complex ion formation** (Exceptionally, black iodine may be pptd, which dissolves only very slowly in excess reagent — see 3, below)	
(a) **Cream**	Ag^+	AgI pptd
(b) **Brown** (really a white ppt that has adsorbed free iodine)	Cu^{2+}	CuI pptd, I_2 liberated, i.e. the redox reaction $2Cu^{2+} + 4I^- \rightarrow 2CuI\downarrow + I_2$
(c) **Yellow** (*N.B. Under extreme conditions, i.e. little ppt and high conc. of I^-, this ppt will dissolve in excess — see 2(a) below*)	Pb^{2+}	PbI_2 pptd
2. PRECIPITATE FORMED, SOLUBLE IN EXCESS REAGENT	**Sparingly soluble iodide pptd dissolving in excess reagent by complex ion formation**	
(a) **Yellow ppt** → colourless soln.	Pb^{2+}	PbI_2 pptd; soluble complex formed, $PbI_2 + 2I^- \rightarrow PbI_4^{2-}$
(b) **Greenish yellow ppt** → very fine grey suspension in colourless soln.	Hg_2^{2+}	Hg_2I_2 pptd; complex ion formed and mercury liberated with excess $Hg_2I_2 + 2I^- \rightarrow HgI_4^{2-} + Hg$
(c) **Red ppt** (**passing through initial yellow stage**) → colourless soln.	Hg^{2+}	HgI_2 pptd; (yellow form meta-stable at room temp.) complex ion formed with excess $HgI_2 + 2I^- \rightarrow HgI_4^{2-}$

3. IODINE LIBERATED	Oxidising agent present (including Cu^{2+} — see 1(b) above, and Fe^{3+})

N.B.

(i) Some oxidising agents, e.g. CrO_4^{2-}, $Cr_2O_7^{2-}$, IO_3^- will only liberate iodine from an iodide in the presence of acid.

(ii) Iodine may be liberated either in soln. or (if concentrations are high) as a black ppt. In soln. it may appear from pale yellow to dark brown, according to concentration. It may be detected

    (a) by boiling the solution or suspension → purple vapour;
    (b) by adding carbon tetrachloride and shaking → pink or purple lower layer;
    (c) by adding starch → deep blue colour.

4. NO APPARENT CHANGE, even after addition of acid	No oxidising agent present. No metal present whose iodide is sparingly soluble

$(CH_3COO)_2Pb$
(see p.26)

TABLE XIII

REACTIONS WITH LEAD(II) ETHANOATE (ACETATE) (or lead(II) nitrate) SOLUTION

Add the reagent, dropwise at first, and then heat gently. Cool.

OBSERVATION	INFERENCE	
	Ion(s) probably present	Probable reaction
1. PRECIPITATE FORMED		
(a) **White**; some or all dissolving on heating, and reprecipitating on cooling	Cl^-, Br^-	$PbCl_2$ or $PbBr_2$ pptd; more soluble in hot water than in cold
White; heating has no effect and ppt is insol. in dil.HNO_3	SO_4^{2-}	$PbSO_4$ pptd
White; heating has no effect but ppt dissolves in dil.HNO_3 with effervescence	CO_3^{2-}	$PbCO_3$ pptd
White; heating has no effect but ppt dissolves in dil.HNO_3 without effervescence	OH^-	$Pb(OH)_2$ pptd
(N.B. If white ppt is initially transient then NaOH or KOH is indicated — the ppt dissolving to give plumbate(II) while the alkali is still in excess. NH_3(aq) indicated by smell — otherwise probably $Ca(OH)_2$ or $Ba(OH)_2$)		
(b) **Yellow**; turning orange on heating	CrO_4^{2-} $Cr_2O_7^{2-}$	$PbCrO_4$ pptd; colour change due to formation of basic salt by hydrolysis
Yellow; no colour change on heating but, if quantity of ppt is small, it may dissolve and then reprecipitate on cooling	I^-	PbI_2 pptd
(c) **Brown** (N.B. Colour may deepen on heating due to dissolving of co-pptd $PbCl_2$; then on cooling a white upper layer is formed as $PbCl_2$ is repptd)	OCl^-	PbO_2 pptd together with some $PbCl_2$; oxidation of lead from Pb(II) to Pb(IV)
2. NO APPARENT EFFECT	NO_3^- CH_3COO^-	No anions present which can yield an insoluble lead compound

TABLE XIV

THE EFFECT OF HEAT ON SOLIDS

The student should use this table with care, bearing in mind that observations may differ according to experimental conditions and methods.

Heat a little of the dry solid in a dry ignition tube. In some cases it may be found more satisfactory to use a test tube to facilitate observation — if sufficient material is available for this and other tests.

For gas tests see Table XV.

OBSERVATION	INFERENCE	
	Ion(s) probably present	Probable reaction
1. GAS OR VAPOUR EVOLVED		
(a) **Moisture condenses on cooler part of tube**	(i) Water of crystallisation present	
	(ii) Hydroxide present (other than those of Na, K)	
	(iii) Basic salt present	
	(iv) Acid salt present	
	(v) Some ammonium salts (e.g. NH_4NO_3) decompose yielding water	
(b) **Colourless gas evolved**		
(i) odourless, relights a glowing splint	higher oxide or oxide of metal below Cu in E.C.S.	Thermal decomposition to lower oxide or metal
(strong heat required — melt gives cream solid on cooling)	NO_3^-	KNO_3, $NaNO_3$ decomposed to nitrite
(black residue gives immediate green soln. when added to NaOH aq)	MnO_4^-	Decomposition to manganate(VI) (MnO_4^{2-}), MnO_2 and O_2
(ii) odourless, turns lime water milky	CO_3^{2-}, or HCO_3^-	Decomposition of carbonate (other than Na, K) or of hydrogencarbonate (only Na, K)
(iii) ammonia	NH_4^+	Thermal decomposition or dissociation of salt (only carbonate, hydrogencarbonate and ethanoate (acetate) are common)

(iv) pungent, fuming in air	Cl^- (Br^-, I^-) hydrated salt	Chloride (as Br^- or I^-) hydrolysed by own water of crystallisation, e.g. $MgCl_2 + H_2O \rightleftharpoons Mg(OH)Cl + HCl$
(v) propanone (acetone) vapour	CH_3COO^-	Thermal decomposition of ethanoate (acetate)
(c) **White choking fumes evolved**	HSO_4^- SO_4^{2-}	Thermal decomposition of hydrogensulphate (lower temp.) or sulphate (higher temp.) to give SO_3
(d) **Brown gas evolved**	NO_3^-	Thermal decomposition of nitrate (other than Na, K, NH_4) to give NO_2
(e) **Purple vapour** (see 2(d) below)		
2. SUBLIMATE FORMED		
(a) **White**	$HgCl_2$ Hg_2Cl_2 NH_4^+	
(b) **Metallic grey**	Hg compound	Decomposition to Hg
(c) **Yellow**, becoming red on rubbing when cool	HgI_2	Metastable polymorph is yellow
(d) **Purplish-black**, dagger-like crystals condensing from purple vapour	I_2 or I^-	If iodide present then oxidising agent also present $2I^- - 2e \rightarrow I_2$
3. SOLID CHANGES COLOUR (*N.B. In some of these changes a gas or vapour is also evolved and a molten step may be evident*)		
(a) **White → yellow**		
(i) melt giving yellow on cooling	Pb^{2+}	PbO formed
(ii) yellow residue turns white again on cooling	Zn^{2+}	ZnO formed which is yellow when hot but white when cold
(b) **White → brown**		
(i) becoming yellow on cooling	Bi^{3+}	Bi_2O_3 formed
(ii) remaining brown on cooling	Cd^{2+}	CdO formed

(c) **Deep pink → blue** (and then black on very strong heating)	Co^{2+}	Hydrated Co^{2+} ion loses water (then black CoO is formed)
(d) **Blue → black**	Cu^{2+}	CuO formed
(e) **Blue → white**	Cu^{2+}	Anhydrous copper(II) salt formed from hydrate
(f) **Green → light brown** (chlorine evolved on strong heating)	Cu^{2+}	Hydrated $CuCl_2$ converted to brown anhydrous salt; $CuCl_2$ converted to CuCl and Cl_2
(g) **Green → black**	Cu^{2+}, Ni^{2+}	Metal oxide MO formed
(h) **Pale green → red-brown** (passing through dirty-white stage, H_2O, SO_2, SO_3 evolved)	$FeSO_4 7H_2O$	Redox reaction, Fe(II) oxidised to Fe(III), as Fe_2O_3, and some $SO_4{}^{2-}$ reduced to SO_2
(j) **Very pale pink → black**	Mn^{2+}	Oxidation of Mn^{2+} to Mn(III) and/or Mn(IV) oxidation states
(k) **Dark brown → yellow** (passes through molten stage — yellow solid on cooling)	PbO_2	Oxygen evolved and Pb(IV) reduced to Pb(II) in PbO
(l) **Red (sometimes dirty yellow → black**, then metallic sublimate	HgO	Hg formed, O_2 evolved
(m) **Orange-red → yellow** (passing through dark-purple stage, melt gives yellow solid on cooling)	Pb_3O_4	Decomposition to PbO; O_2 evolved
(n) **Buff → red-brown**	Fe^{3+}	Decomposition to Fe_2O_3
(o) **Orange (crystalline) → green** (much gas evolved and many sparks observed)	$Cr_2O_7{}^{2-}$ as $(NH_4)_2Cr_2O_7$	Products are N_2, H_2O and Cr_2O_3

N.B. Compounds with organic anions (e.g. CH_3COO^-) frequently give black residues on heating — see *Organic Reactions*, Table V.

4. SOLID DOES NOT CHANGE COLOUR	**Either solid is thermally stable and does not have polymorphs of different colour, or solid product has same colour as original**
	(Thermal stability is associated with metal oxides and sulphates. A white solid which does not change colour on heating may contain Na^+, K^+, Ba^{2+}, Ca^{2+}, Mg^{2+}) Sn^{4+}

TABLE XV

TESTS FOR GASES AND VAPOURS

GAS or VAPOUR	COLOUR, ODOUR	TEST	RESULT IF POSITIVE
NH_3	Colourless, pungent	Moist red litmus paper	Turns blue
CO_2	Colourless, odourless	Bubble through lime water	Turns milky
SO_2	Colourless, pungent	Bubble through acidified (dil. H_2SO_4) dichromate soln.	Turns orange $\rightarrow$ green, but no ppt
H_2S	Colourless, bad eggs	Moist lead(II) ethanoate (acetate) paper	Turns black
H_2	Colourless, odourless	Ignite N.B. This is not a conclusive test — other gases behave similarly, particularly CO	Burns with very pale blue flame; may be mildly explosive
O_2	Colourless, odourless	Glowing splint	Ignites or glows much brighter
HCl HBr HI	Colourless, pungent	(a) Blow across mouth of test-tube (b) Bring into contact with drop of ammonia soln. on a glass rod	Copious fuming White fumes of NH_4Cl, etc.

N.B. (i) All acid gases and vapours and the halogens give white fumes with ammonia so this test should not be regarded as conclusive.

(ii) HBr is usually accompanied by red-brown bromine vapour; HI is usually accompanied by black precipitated iodine which gives purple vapours on heating

Cl_2	Yellow-green, pungent	(a) Moist litmus paper (b) Bubble through KBr aq.	Bleached Br_2 liberated — soln. turning yellow or orange
Br_2	Red-brown; pungent; condensing to brown liquid	Bubble through water, then add a little NaOH aq. to this soln.	Yellow-orange aqueous soln. becomes colourless on addition of alkali
CrO_2Cl_2	Red-brown; pungent; condensing to red liquid fumes in air		Yellow-orange aqueous soln. remains yellow on addition of alkali
NO_2	Brown; pungent		Colourless aqueous soln.; no colour change on addition of alkali
NO_2 (additional test)		Bubble through fresh $FeSO_4$ aq.	Brown coloration of $Fe(NO)^{2+}$ complex ion
I_2	Violet; pungent; condensing to black dagger-like crystals		

FLAME
(see p.32)

TABLE XVI

FLAME TESTS

Flame tests are normally best performed on halides because these are the most volatile of salts.

If testing a solid, moisten a clean platinum or nichrome wire with concentrated hydrochloric acid and bring into contact with the solid so that some of the latter adheres to the wire. Hold the wire in the edge of a non-luminous bunsen flame.

If testing a solution, treat a little of this with one drop of concentrated hydrochloric acid, moisten the wire with the mixture, and hold in the bunsen flame.

N.B. (i) If potassium is suspected the flame should be observed through cobalt-blue glass (this filters off wavelengths which interfere with observation — particularly the yellow of sodium).

(ii) If a non-expendable wire is used it must be thoroughly cleaned by alternately placing it in concentrated hydrochloric acid **(not the reagent bottle)** and the bunsen flame.

COLOUR OF FLAME	ION PROBABLY PRESENT
Red	Li^+
Crimson	Sr^{2+}
Brick-red	Ca^{2+}
Yellow	Na^+ often interferes with others
Green (apple)	Ba^{2+}
(bluish)	Cu^{2+}
Lilac (purple through blue glass)	K^+

TABLE XVII

CONFIRMATORY TESTS FOR CATIONS

ION	TEST	RESULT IF POSITIVE
Aluminium Al^{3+}	(a) To soln. add 1 or 2 drops of litmus soln. and then dil.HCl until acid (if not already); then add NH_3 (aq) until just alkaline	Blue lake obtained (hydroxide pptd, adsorbing dye to leave soln. almost colourless)
	(b) To 2 or 3ml of soln. add 1 drop of cobalt(II) nitrate soln. Moisten a piece of filter paper with this mixture and heat the paper strongly by playing a flame on it direct (on a tripod or soft asbestos sheet)	Bright blue ash of cobalt(II) aluminate
	(c) See note at end of table on white hydroxides	
Ammonium NH_4^+	(a) Warm gently a little soln. (or solid) with a slight excess of NaOH aq.	Ammonia evolved (turning moist red litmus paper blue — take care to avoid splashes of NaOH aq. onto paper)
	A more sensitive test on solid:	
	(b) Grind a little solid with soda-lime and 1 drop of water	As above
Antimony Sb^{3+}	(a) Pass H_2S into acid soln. (*N.B. if acid too concentrated ppt forms only on dilution*)	Orange-red ppt of Sb_2S_3
	(b) Add yellow ammonium sulphide soln.	Orange-red ppt of Sb_2S_3 soluble in excess to give ammonium thioantimonate (cf. tin(IV) — but SnS_2 lighter in colour than Sb_2S_3)
	(c) Pour a little of the soln. into a large quantity of distilled water	White ppt of basic salt (SbOCl) (cf. bismuth)
	(d) See note at end of table on white hydroxides	

Barium Ba^{2+}	(a) To soln. add K_2CrO_4 soln. (b) Flame test — see table XVI, p.32	Yellow ppt of $BaCrO_4$ (cf. lead, but $BaCrO_4$ is much paler in colour than $PbCrO_4$; also Ba^{2+} does not give an insol. iodide like PbI_2 on treating with KI aq.)
Bismuth Bi^{3+}	(a) To soln. add sodium stannate(II) soln. ($SnCl_2$ aq. + excess NaOH aq., i.e. white ppt of $Sn(OH)_2$ dissolves) (b) Pour a little soln. into a large quantity of distilled water (c) To soln. add NaOH aq. and heat (see also note at end of table on white hydroxides)	Black ppt of finely divided bismuth metal, stannate(II) oxidised to stannate(IV) (cf. silver) White ppt of basic salt (usually BiOCl) (cf. antimony) White ppt of $Bi(OH)_3$ turning yellow on heating due to partial dehydration
Cadmium Cd^{2+}	(a) Pass H_2S into acid soln. (*N.B. if acid too concentrated ppt forms only on dilution*) (b) See note at end of table on white hydroxides	Yellow ppt of CdS (insoluble in yellow ammonium sulphide) (cf. tin(IV))
Calcium Ca^{2+}	Flame test — see Table XVI, p.32	
Chromium (III) Cr^{3+}	(a) To soln. add excess NaOH aq. to dissolve initial grey-green ppt (giving dark green chromite). Then add H_2O_2 (oxidises chromite to yellow chromate) followed by pentanol (amyl alcohol) and dil. H_2SO_4. Shake gently (b) Fuse solid with large excess of fusion mixture (Na_2CO_3/KNO_3)	Blue colour of CrO_5 concentrat- ing in organic layer Yellow mass of chromate (CrO_4^{2-}) obtained
Cobalt(II) Co^{2+}	To soln. add a little conc.HCl, then solid NH_4CNS and some pentanol (amyl alcohol). Shake gently	Blue upper layer obtained (sometimes pinkish-purple) (cobalt(II) thiocyanic acid $H_2Co(CNS)_4$)

Copper(II) Cu^{2+}	(a) To soln. add excess NH_3 (aq) soln,	Initial $Cu(OH)_2$ ppt dissolves to give deep blue soln. containing $Cu(NH_3)_4^{2+}$ ions (cf. nickel)
	(b) To soln. add potassium hexacyanoferrate(II) soln.	Brownish-red gelatinous ppt of $Cu_2[Fe(CN)_6]$
	(c) Flame test — see Table XVI, p.32	
Iron(III) Fe^{3+}	(a) To soln. add a crystal (or soln.) of NH_4CNS	Very deep blood-red coloration. *(N.B. All iron(II) salt solns. contain some Fe^{3+} ions (due to aerial oxidation) and will give a faint red colour with this test)*
	(b) To soln. add NaOH aq.	Red-brown gelatinous ppt of $Fe(OH)_3$
Iron(II) Fe^{2+}	(a) To soln. add a few drops of potassium hexacyanoferrate(III) soln.	Deep blue ppt
	(b) To soln. add NaOH aq.	Muddy-green gelatinous ppt of $Fe(OH)_2$, turning brown at surface
Lead Pb^{2+}	(a) To soln. add K_2CrO_4 aq.	Yellow ppt of $PbCrO_4$ turning orange on heating (cf. barium)
	(b) To soln. add KI aq.	Yellow ppt of PbI_2
	(c) See note at end of table on white hydroxides	
Magnesium Mg^{2+}	There is no satisfactory simple confirmatory test for Mg^{2+} ions. See note at end of table on white hydroxides	
Manganese Mn^{2+}	(a) To soln. add a little conc.HNO_3 followed by a little solid sodium bismuthate(V)	Purple soln. of MnO_4^- ions obtained

	(b) Fuse solid with a large excess of fusion mixture (Na_2CO_3/KNO_3)	Green mass of manganate(VI) MnO_4^{2-} obtained
	(c) To soln. add NH_4Cl, NH_3(aq) till alkaline and then pass H_2S	Flesh coloured ppt of MnS obtained
Mercury(II) Hg^{2+}	(a) To soln. add KI aq.	Red ppt of HgI_2 (passing through initial metastable yellow form) soluble in excess to give a colourless soln. of HgI_4^{2-} ions
	(b) To soln. add NaOH aq.	Yellow ppt of HgO
Mercury(I) Hg_2^{2+}	(a) To soln. add KI aq.	Yellow-green ppt of Hg_2I_2 soluble in excess to give a colourless soln. of HgI_4^{2-} ions containing a fine grey ppt of mercury
	(b) Add dil.HCl then excess NH_3(aq)	White ppt of Hg_2Cl_2 turning black with ammonia (finely divided mercury)
Mercury i.e. either Hg^{2+} or Hg_2^{2+}	(a) To soln. add $SnCl_2$ aq.	White ppt of Hg_2Cl_2 turning grey, then black (may need warming) as Hg_2Cl_2 is reduced to mercury
	(b) Mix solid with anhydrous Na_2CO_3, then heat in an ignition tube (Care — poisonous vapour)	Grey sublimate of Hg forming globules when rubbed with a glass rod
Nickel Ni^{2+}	(a) Make soln. just alkaline with NH_3(aq) and then add dimethyl-glyoxime reagent (N.B. Cu^{2+}, Fe^{2+}, Co^{2+} must be absent)	Red ppt of complex nickel dimethyl-glyoxime
	(b) To soln. add excess NH_3(aq)	Initial pale green ppt of $Ni(OH)_2$ (frequently not seen if Ni^{2+} soln. is dilute) dissolves in excess to give deep blue $Ni(NH_3)_4^{2+}$ ions — similar to copper

Potassium K^+	(a) Flame test — see Table XVI, p.32	
	(b) To soln. add $Na_3Co(NO_2)_6$ aq. (*N.B. NH_4^+ ions must be absent*)	Yellow ppt of $K_3Co(NO_2)_6$
Silver Ag^+	(a) To neutral soln. add K_2CrO_4 aq.	Brick-red ppt of Ag_2CrO_4
	(b) Add soln. to sodium stannate(II) soln. ($SnCl_2$ aq. + excess NaOH aq.)	Black ppt of metallic silver (cf. bismuth)
	(c) To soln. add NH_3(aq) until Ag_2O ppt dissolves. Add Fehling's B soln. and warm gently. *If test is to be performed on AgCl ppt,* first boil this with NaOH aq. to convert to Ag_2O. Decant off NaOH. Add NH_3(aq) to dissolve ppt. Add Fehling's B soln. and warm gently	Silver mirror deposited on in- side of test-tube
Sodium Na^+	Flame test — see Table XVI, p.32	
Tin(IV) Sn^{4+}	(a) If no reaction with $HgCl_2$ take a fresh portion of soln., add a little conc. HCl and iron wire and boil, then add $HgCl_2$ aq.	White ppt of Hg_2Cl_2 reduced to black mercury (see Sn^{2+} below)
	(b) Pass H_2S into acid soln.	Yellow ppt of SnS_2 soluble in yellow ammonium sulphide (cf. cadmium)
	(c) See note at end of table on white hydroxides	
Tin(II) Sn^{2+}	(a) To soln. add 1 or 2 drops of $HgCl_2$ aq. (*Sn^{2+} must be in excess*)	White ppt of Hg_2Cl_2 turning grey, then black (may need warming) as Hg_2Cl_2 is reduced to Hg
	(b) To soln. add excess NaOH aq. to give stannate(II) soln. then add $AgNO_3$aq. (*N.B. a Bi^{3+} soln. could be used instead* *of Ag^+ — black Bi obtained*)	Black ppt of Ag

	(c) Pass H_2S into acid soln.	Brown ppt of SnS soluble in yellow ammonium sulphide
	(d) See note at end of table on white hydroxides	
Zinc Zn^{2+}	(a) To soln. add 1 or 2 drops of NH_3(aq) (care to avoid excess). Evaporate the suspension in an evaporating basin and ignite (play flame on to residue direct)	White ppt of $Zn(OH)_2$ gives ZnO which is yellow when hot turning white on cooling
	(b) To soln. add NH_4Cl then NH_3(aq) pass H_2S	White (often dirty white) ppt of ZnS
	(c) See note at end of table on white hydroxides	

SPARINGLY SOLUBLE WHITE HYDROXIDES

The experimenter may find the following table useful for distinguishing between sparingly soluble white hydroxides. $Ba(OH)_2$ and $Ca(OH)_2$ have not been included because they are borderline cases which are rarely encountered as precipitates with the concentrations of solutions normally used. $Mn(OH)_2$, also, is not included because this is readily recognised by rapid aerial oxidation to a brown Mn(III) compound.

Hydroxide	Pptd by NaOH(aq.)	Sol. in excess NaOH(aq.)	Pptd by NH$_3$(aq)	Sol. in excess NH$_3$(aq)	Pptd by NH$_3$(aq) in presence of NH$_4^+$	Colour of Sulphide	Sulphide pptd by H$_2$S from
Mg(OH)$_2$	●		slight				not pptd
Bi(OH)$_3$	●		●		●	Brown	acid soln.
Cd(OH)$_2$	●		●	●	●	Yellow	all solns.
Zn(OH)$_2$	●	●	●	●		White	alkaline soln.
Al(OH)$_3$	●	●	●		●		not pptd
Sn(OH)$_2$	●	●	●		●	Brown	⎫
Sn(OH)$_4$	●	●	●		●	Yellow	⎬ acid soln.
Sb(OH)$_3$	●	●	●		●	Orange	⎭
Pb(OH)$_2$	●	●	●		●*	Black	all solns.

*N.B. If NH$_4$Cl is used this will partially precipitate Pb^{2+} as PbCl$_2$ – addition of NH$_3$(aq) then causes precipitation of Pb(OH)$_2$ from the supernatant solution.

TABLE XVIII

CONFIRMATORY TESTS FOR ANIONS

ION	TEST	RESULT IF POSITIVE
Chloride Cl^-	Silver nitrate test for a halide: To the soln. add dil.HNO_3 and then $AgNO_3$ aq.	White ppt of AgCl going curdy; greying in bright light
Bromide Br^-		Pale cream ppt of AgBr going curdy; greying in bright light
Iodide I^-		Rich cream ppt of AgI going curdy; greying only very slowly in bright light

N.B. *If the silver nitrate test is positive it is advisable to perform a further confirmatory test for the ion suspected to be present since it is difficult to differentiate between the silver halide precipitates — particularly AgBr and AgI. The following test will normally prove conclusive, though others are given below*

Halide present, i.e. Cl^-, Br^- or I^-	To solution add one or two drops of chlorine water (or slightly acidified hypochlorite) followed by 2 or 3 cm^3 of CCl_4. Shake	(a) Colourless or very pale green lower layer indicates Cl^- — this being unaffected by the reagent (b) Orange lower layer indicates Br^- — this being oxidised to Br_2 (c) Pink or purple lower layer indicates I^- — this being oxidised to I_2
Chloride Cl^-	(a) Silver nitrate test (see above) (b) To solid add conc. H_2SO_4 and warm (c) Mix solid with MnO_2 and add conc. H_2SO_4. Warm if necessary (d) Mix solid with solid $K_2Cr_2O_7$, add conc. H_2SO_4 and warm. Pass any	Pungent, colourless, HCl evolved, fuming heavily in air Chlorine evolved — pale green gas which bleaches damp litmus paper Red-brown vapours of CrO_2Cl_2 giving

	red-brown fumes into water and add lead(II) ethanoate (acetate) aq. (Detects Cl⁻in presence of Br⁻)	chromic acid' with water and then yellow lead(II) chromate. If red-brown fumes were Br_2, white lead(II) bromide would be obtained
Bromide Br^-	(a) Silver nitrate test (see above)	
	(b) Chlorine water/CCl_4 test (see above)	
	(c) To solid add conc. H_2SO_4 and warm	Mixture of fuming HBr and red-brown Br_2 evolved
Iodide I^-	(a) Silver nitrate test (see above)	
	(b) Chlorine water/CCl_4 test (see above)	
	(c) To solid add conc. H_2SO_4 and warm	Black ppt of I_2 formed and fuming HI evolved; violet I_2 vapour observed on warming
Carbonate CO_3^{2-} and Hydrogen carbonate HCO_3^-	(a) To solid or soln. add dil.HCl	Effervescence; colourless gas turning lime water milky
	(b) Heat the solid (not a good test because K_2CO_3 and Na_2CO_3 do not decompose, and $BaCO_3$ and $CaCO_3$ require very high temperatures)	Colourless gas evolved turning lime water milky *N.B. A condensate of water in the upper part of the test-tube does not necessarily indicate a hydrogencarbonate — basic carbonates usually give this too.*
	To differentiate between CO_3^{2-} and HCO_3^- (all hydrogencarbonates are soluble in water and only those of sodium, potassium and ammonium are ordinarily obtainable as solids)	
	To the **unheated** test soln. add a drop or two of $MgSO_4$ aq.	(a) A white ppt (of $MgCO_3$) indicates CO_3^{2-} (b) No ppt indicates HCO_3^- — $Mg(HCO_3)_2$ being soluble
Sulphite SO_3^{2-}	To solid or soln. add dil.HCl and warm	Pungent SO_2 evolved (turning acid dichromate green) but no S pptd

Thiosulphate $S_2O_3^{2-}$	(a) To solid or soln. add dil.HCl and warm	White or cream ppt of S accompanied by evolution of SO_2 (pungent and turning acid dichromate green)
	(b) To soln. add few drops of $FeCl_3$ aq.	Purple coloration (thought to be $Fe(S_2O_3)_2^-$ ions) slowly disappearing. Overall redox reaction: $$2Fe^{3+} + 2S_2O_3^{2-} \rightarrow 2Fe^{2+} + S_4O_6^{2-}$$
	(c) To a **neutral** soln. add iodine soln.	Iodine colour disappears due to redox reaction $$I_2 + 2S_2O_3^{2-} \rightarrow 2I^- + S_4O_6^{2-}$$
Sulphide S^{2-}	(a) To soln. add $(CH_3COO)_2Pb$ aq.	Black ppt — of PbS
	(b) To soln. add Cd^{2+} soln.	Yellow ppt — of CdS
	(c) To solid or soln. add dil.HCl (Warm if necessary)	H_2S evolved, blackening damp lead(II) ethanoate (acetate) paper
Sulphate SO_4^{2-} and Hydrogen sulphate HSO_4^-	(a) To soln. add dil.HCl and then $BaCl_2$ aq.	White ppt — of $BaSO_4$
	(b) To soln. add dil.HNO_3 and then one drop of $(CH_3COO)_2Pb$ aq. Warm	White ppt of $PbSO_4$ unaffected by heating — chloride would dissolve
	To differentiate between SO_4^{2-} and HSO_4^- (all hydrogensulphates are soluble in water and only those of sodium, potassium and ammonium are ordinarily obtainable as solids)	
	(i) Heat the solid	(a) Dense choking white fumes of SO_3 obtained readily indicates HSO_4^-
		(b) SO_3 fumes only on very strong heating indicates SO_4^{2-}
	(ii) To soln. add solid Na_2CO_3	(a) Vigorous effervescence of CO_2 indicates HSO_4^-
		(b) Slight or no effervescence indicates SO_4^{2-}

Nitrate NO_3^-	(a) 'Brown ring' test To soln. add cold, freshly prepared $FeSO_4$ aq. Then pour conc. H_2SO_4 carefully down inside of test-tube to form lower layer	Brown ring formed at interface

N.B. (i) Iodides and bromides also give brown rings with this test, and nitrites give a brown coloration throughout the soln. The student is advised to perform this test on solns. known to contain NO_3^-, I^-, Br^- and NO_2^- and compare the results. The iodide brown ring usually has a slight purplish tinge at the bottom; the bromide brown ring is a rich orange-brown. The I^- and Br^- brown rings are due to liberated halogen; that of NO_3^- is due to the formation of the complex ion $Fe(NO)^{2+}$ by the following reactions

$$NO_3^- + H_2SO_4 \rightarrow H^+ + NO_3^- + HSO_4^-$$
$$4H^+ + NO_3^- + 3Fe^{2+} \rightarrow 3Fe^{3+} + NO + 2H_2O$$
$$Fe^{2+} + NO \rightarrow Fe(NO)^{2+}$$

   (ii) If a cation is present which gives an insoluble sulphate, e.g. Pb^{2+}, Cu^{2+}, Ba^{2+}, Hg_2^{2+}, a white ppt is obtained on addition of $FeSO_4$ aq. However, this does not affect the brown ring reaction.

	(b) To **cold** soln. or solid add a few copper turnings and then conc. H_2SO_4. Warm	Brown oxides of nitrogen obtained and a blue soln. formed (*N.B. nitrites give immediate effervescence before warming*)
Nitrite NO_2^-	(a) To solid or conc. soln. add dil. HCl	Immediate effervescence; pale blue soln; brown NO_2 evolved
	(b) To cold soln. add $FeSO_4$ aq. followed by dil. H_2SO_4	Dark brown complex ion $Fe(NO)^{2+}$ formed
Phosphates PO_4^{3-} HPO_4^{2-} $H_2PO_4^-$	(a) To soln. add a little conc. HNO_3 followed by ammonium molybdate soln. Warm very gently (b) To soln. add $FeCl_3$ aq.	Yellow ppt of ammonium phosphomolybdate Cream ppt of $FePO_4$
Chromate CrO_4^{2-}	To soln. add dil. H_2SO_4 See also over page	Colour change from yellow to orange, i.e. dichromate formed

Dichromate $Cr_2O_7{}^{2-}$	To soln. add NaOH aq. See also below	Colour change from orange to yellow, i.e. chromate formed
Chromate $CrO_4{}^{2-}$ and Dichromate $Cr_2O_7{}^{2-}$	Both give the following reactions (a) To soln. add $(\dot{C}H_3COO)_2Pb$ aq. (b) To soln. add $AgNO_3$ aq. (c) To soln. add H_2O_2, amyl alcohol (pentanol) and then dil.H_2SO_4	Yellow $PbCrO_4$ pptd Brick red Ag_2CrO_4 pptd Blue CrO_5 formed, concentrating in alcohol layer
Ethanoate (Acetate) CH_3COO^-	To solid or soln. add dil.H_2SO_4. Warm	Smell of vinegar from displaced weak acid CH_3COOH

EXERCISES

1. Solids C, D, and E are lead(II) nitrate, cobalt(II) chloride and ammonium bromide (not necessarily in that order).
   Perform tests (a) and (b) on small portions of each solid. Then prepare solutions of the solids in distilled water and perform test (c) on each.
   Describe fully your methods and observations (in the form of a table as shown). Identify C, D and E and elucidate any reactions observed.

	C	D	E
(a) Heat in an ignition tube			
(b) Conc. sulphuric acid			
(c) Sodium hydroxide solution			

2. G, H and J are three colourless, crystalline salts. Perform tests, with the reagents indicated, on solutions of these salts in distilled water.
   Give a full account of your methods and observations (tabulated as shown) and identify the anions of G, H and J. Give your reasons for the identifications you make.

	G	H	J
(a) Dilute hydrochloric acid			
(b) Barium chloride solution to solution resulting from (a)			
(c) Sodium carbonate solution			

3. The given salts W, X and Y are potassium nitrate, potassium bromide and potassium iodide (not necessarily in that order).
   Perform test (a) on small portions of the solids and tests (b) and (c) on solutions of the solids in distilled water.
   Describe in full (using a table of the type shown) your methods and observations and identify W, X and Y, giving reasons for your conclusions. Perform a further test on each substance (or its aqueous solution) to confirm your conclusions.

	W	X	Y
(a) Conc. sulphuric acid			
(b) Silver nitrate solution			
(c) 'Brown Ring' test			
(d) Further test			

4. K, L and M are simple salts.

Prepare solutions of these salts in distilled water and perform tests with the reagents indicated.

Give a full tabulated account of your methods and observations. Draw what inferences you can about K, L and M and the reactions observed, giving your reasons. (N.B. A complete identification is not necessarily required.)

	K	L	M
Sodium hydroxide solution			
Ammonia solution			
Dilute sulphuric acid			

5. Perform the tests indicated in the table on the salts T, U and V.

Describe in full your methods and observations (use a table of the kind shown) and draw what conclusions you can about T, U and V — a complete identification is not possible.

	T	U	V
(a) Dilute nitric acid on solid (test for gases evolved)			
(b) Barium chloride solution to solution obtained in (a)			
(c) Magnesium sulphate solution on a solution of the unknown made in cold distilled water			

6. Solids Q, R and S are copper(II) sulphate, nickel(II) sulphate and mercury(II) chloride (not necessarily in that order).

Prepare solutions of these salts and perform tests on them with the reagents indicated.

Give a full, tabulated account of your methods and observations and identify the salts. Perform a further test on each solution to positively identify the metal ion present.

Elucidate all of the reactions you observe.

	Q	R	S
Ammonia solution			
Sodium hydroxide solution and warm			
Hydrogen sulphide, then add ammonia solution			
Further test			

7. Prepare solutions of the salts N, O and P in distilled water to which a little dilute nitric acid has been added.

Test the solutions with the reagents indicated and draw what conclusions you can about the nature of the salts. Devise and perform one other test in each case by way of further investigation.

Your account should be tabulated and must include full details of your methods and observations. Your conclusions should be backed by good reasons.

	N	O	P
Potassium chromate solution and warm			
Dilute hydrochloric acid and warm			
Potassium iodide solution			
Further test			

8. Solutions D, E and F are iron(III) chloride, bromine and potassium chromate (not necessarily in that order) in aqueous solution.

Perform tests on these solutions with the reagents indicated. Identify D, E and F and elucidate the observed reactions.

Your methods, observations and elucidations should be given in full, in tabular form.

	D	E	F
Dilute sulphuric acid			
Sodium hydroxide solution			
Potassium iodide solution, followed by dilute sulphuric acid			
Tin(II) chloride solution			

9. F, G and H are simple salts.

Prepare solutions of the salts in distilled water and test these solutions with the reagents indicate in the table.

Describe fully your methods and observations (use a table of the type shown) and draw what inferences you can about the cations present and the reactions observed, giving your reasons. Perform not more than two further tests in each case to confirm your ideas.

	F	G	H
Sodium hydroxide solution			
Sodium hypochlorite solution, and then warm			
Silver sulphate solution			
Further tests (i) (ii)			

10. Z, A and B are aqueous solutions of simple salts.

Test portions of these solutions with the reagents indicated, giving a full, tabulated account of your methods and observations.

From your observations draw what conclusions you can about the nature of the dissolved solids — giving your reasons.

	Z	A	B
Large quantity of water			
Ammonia solution			
Sodium hydroxide solution			
Yellow ammonium sulphide solution			

11. J, K and L are sulphates of three transition metals.

Prepare aqueous solutions of the salts and test portions of them with the reagents indicated in the table.

Draw what conclusions you can about the nature of the cations present and then perform one further test on each solution to positively identify the cation.

Give a full account of your methods and observations (use a table of the type shown) and elucidate all reactions you observe.

	J	K	L
Sodium hydroxide solution			
Sodium carbonate solution			
A little solid sodium peroxide			
Further test			

12. Prepare aqueous solutions of the three simple salts A, B and C, and test portions of these solutions with the reagents indicated.

Make what inferences you can about the nature of the reactions you observe and about A, B and C.

Give a full account of your methods and observations (tabulated) and give full reasons for the conclusions you draw.

	A	B	C
Sodium hydroxide solution			
Hydrogen sulphide			
Tin(II) chloride followed by sodium hydroxide solution			
Further test to positively identify the cation			

13. You are given three salts M, N and O.

Perform, on portions of them, the tests indicated in the table.

Draw what conclusions you can about the salts and about the reactions you observe, and perform one further test on each salt (or its aqueous solution) by way of further investigation.

Give a full account of your methods and observations and give reasons for the conclusions you draw. Your account should be in the form of a table as shown.

	M	N	O
Flame test			
Dilute sulphuric acid on a solution of the salt in distilled water			
Further test			

14. Prepare aqueous solutions of each of the salts X, Y and Z. Test portions of these solutions with the reagents indicated.

Make what inferences you can about the salts and about the reactions that you observe.

Give a full account (tabulated) of your methods, observations and inferences.

	X	Y	Z
Sodium carbonate solution			
Sodium hydroxide solution			
Solid ammonium chloride followed by ammonia solution			

15. Prepare a solution of A in distilled water and test separate portions of the solution with (a) sodium hydroxide solution and (b) dilute hydrochloric acid followed by barium chloride solution.

Describe as fully as you can all that you do and observe, and draw conclusions about the nature of the ions present. Your account should be tabulated.

Devise, perform and report on two further tests which will enable you to identify the ion which is not positively identified by tests (a) and (b).

Test	Method and observations	Inferences
(a) Sodium hydroxide solution		
(b) Dilute hydrochloric acid, followed by barium chloride solution		
(c) Further tests (i) (ii)		

16. B is a simple salt. Prepare a solution of this salt in distilled water.

Describe the behaviour of this solution when separate portions are treated with (a) sodium hydroxide solution, (b) ammonium chloride followed by ammonia solution. Describe also the effect of (c) hydrogen sulphide on the solution obtained in test (b).

Draw what conclusions you can about the nature of (b) and about the reactions you observe. Your account should be in the form of a table, as below.

Test	Method and observations	Inferences
(a) Sodium hydroxide solution		
(b) Ammonium chloride followed by ammonia solution		
(c) Solution from (b) treated with hydrogen sulphide		
(d) Further test		

17. C is a solution of a simple salt.

To separate portions of this solution add (a) potassium iodide solution, (b) a piece of copper wire.

Describe in full, in tabular form, all that you do and observe. Draw what inferences you can from your observations. Carry out and report on two further tests to confirm your conclusions.

Test	Method and observations	Inferences
(a) Potassium iodide solution		
(b) A piece of copper wire		
(c) Further tests (i) (ii)		

18. The substance G is ammonium iron(II) sulphate.

The substance H is a simple salt.

Prepare a solution of H in distilled water and describe as carefully and as fully as you can the behaviour of this solution (a) with a solution of ammonium chloride (b) with dilute ammonia solution (c) when it is warmed with a solution of the ammonium iron(II) sulphate.

What tentative inferences can be drawn from the results of these experiments? Carry out and report on TWO experiments to test these inferences.

Full credit will not be given unless your methods, observations and the deductions from them are fully and accurately reported.

The record of your work must be made in the form of a table as follows:

Test	Method and observations	Inferences
(a) Solution of ammonium chloride		
(b) Dilute ammonia solution		
(c) Warmed with solution of ammonium iron(II) sulphate		
Experiments (1) (2)		

(L)

19. You are provided with two solids P and Q, each being a simple salt. Mix a little of each separately with a small quantity of potassium dichromate crystals, and then warm with concentrated sulphuric acid.

Describe as carefully and as fully as you can, the reactions you observe, and state any tentative inferences that can be drawn from this.

For each substance P and Q carry out TWO further experiments to test your inferences and report your findings.

Full credit will not be given unless your methods, observations and the deductions from them are fully and accurately reported.

The record of your work must be made in the form of tables as follows:

SUBSTANCE P

Test	Method and observations	Inferences
Mix with some crystals of potassium dichromate and then warm with concentrated sulphuric acid		
Further tests (1) (2)		

SUBSTANCE Q

Table as above

(L)

20. The solutions G and H each contain a simple salt dissolved in dilute hydrochloric acid.

Describe as carefully as you can the action upon each of them of (a) sodium hydroxide solution (b) hydrogen sulphide gas. What tentative inferences can be drawn from your observations? Describe ONE further test that would enable you to distinguish between G and H. Carry out the test and report on it.

Full credit will not be given unless your methods, observations and the deductions from them are fully and accurately reported.

The record of your work must be made in the form of tables as follows:

SOLUTION G

Test	Method and observations	Inferences
Caustic soda solution		
Hydrogen sulphide gas		
Further test		

SOLUTION H

Table as above

(L)

21. You are provided with two substances C and D, each of which is a simple salt. Dissolve them separately in distilled water. Describe as carefully as you can the reaction of each of the solutions so obtained with

(a) potassium iodide solution

(b) a stream of hydrogen sulphide gas

What tentative inferences can be drawn from your observations?

For each substance carry out and report on ONE further experiment to test these inferences.

Full credit will not be given unless your methods, observations and the deductions from them are fully and accurately reported.

The record of your work must be made in the form of tables as follows:

SOLUTION OF C

Test	Method and observations	Inferences
(a) Potassium iodide solution		
(b) Hydrogen sulphide gas		
(c) Experiments to test your inferences		

SOLUTION OF D

Table as above

(L)

22. You are provided with two substances L and M, each of which is a simple salt. Dissolve them separately in distilled water, mix the solutions, collect the precipitate formed, X, and wash it.
Describe as carefully and as fully as you can the behaviour of this precipitate, X, when:
   (a) it is suspended in water and treated with sodium hydroxide pellets until no further change occurs.
   (b) dilute sulphuric acid is added to a portion of the solution obtained in reaction (a).
What tentative inferences can be drawn from your observations?
For each of the substances L and M carry out and report on TWO experiments to test these inferences.
Full credit will not be given unless your methods, observations, and deductions from them are fully and accurately reported.
The record of your work must be made in the form of tables as follows:

PRECIPITATE X

Test	Method and observations	Inferences
(a) Sodium hydroxide on precipitate X		
(b) Dilute sulphuric acid added to part of solution obtained in (a)		

SUBSTANCE L

Test	Method and observations	Inferences
Experiments to test your inferences (1) (2)		

SUBSTANCE M

Table as for substance L above

(L)

53

23. You are provided with two different substances, C and D, each of which is a simple salt. Dissolve them separately in distilled water, and to each solution add aqueous ammonia and ammonium chloride. Describe as carefully and as fully as you can the action upon the solutions so obtained the action of (a) hydrogen sulphide gas (b) saturated calcium sulphate solution.

What tentative inferences can be drawn from your observations?

For each solution of C and D carry out and report on TWO further experiments to test these inferences.

Full credit will not be given unless your methods, observations and the deductions from them are fully and accurately reported.

The record of your work must be made in the form of tables as follows:

SUBSTANCE C

Test	Method and observations	Inference
(a) Hydrogen sulphide gas gas		
(b) Saturated calcium sulphate solution		
Further Experiments (1) (2)		

SUBSTANCE D

Table as above

(L)

24. The red powder C provided is mercury(II) oxide. It is insoluble in water. D is a simple salt.

(a) Dissolve D in distilled water and test the solution so obtained with litmus paper.

(b) Add an excess of the solution D to a little of the mercury(II) oxide and again test the solution with litmus paper.

Describe as carefully and as fully as you can:

(c) the behaviour of the solution of mercury(II) oxide in S when it is warmed with acidified potassium dichromate solution, and

(d) what is observed when the products of the reaction (c) are treated with an excess of sodium thiosulphate crystals.

What tentative inferences can be drawn from your observations?

Carry out and describe TWO experiments to test these inferences. Full credit will not be given unless your methods, observations, and the deductions from them are fully and accurately reported.

The record of your work must be made in the form of a table as follows:

SUBSTANCE D

Test	Method and observations	Inferences
(a) Solution of D tested with litmus		
(b) Solution of mercury(II) oxide in D tested with litmus		
(c) Solution of mercury(II) oxide in D boiled with potassium dichromate		
(d) Reaction products of (c) treated with excess of sodium thiosulphate crystals		
Experiments to test your inferences (1) (2)		

(L)

25. The solutions L and M each contain the chloride of a metal dissolved in dilute hydrochloric acid. Describe as fully and as carefully as you can the reactions that occur when each is treated with (a) distilled water, (b) a solution of mercury(II) chloride.

What tentative inferences can be drawn from your observations?

For each solution of L and M carry out and report on TWO further experiments that would enable you to test these inferences. Full credit will not be given unless your methods, observations and the deductions from them are fully and accurately reported.

The record of your work must be made in the form of tables as follows:

SOLUTION L

Test	Method and observations	Inferences
(a) Distilled water		
(b) A solution of mercury(II) chloride		
Further tests (1) (2)		

SOLUTION M

Table as above

(L)

55

A SPECIMEN QUESTION AND PRACTICAL ACCOUNT

QUESTION

You are provided with two substances C and D, each of which is a simple salt. Dissolve them separately in distilled water.

Describe as carefully and as fully as you can the behaviour of each of the solutions so obtained with (a) potassium chromate solution, (b) dilute sulphuric acid.

Mix hot, dilute solutions of C and D, cool the mixture, observe what happens and report on it (c). What tentative inferences can be drawn from your observations?

For each solution of C and D carry out and report on TWO experiments that would enable you to test these inferences.

Full credit will not be given unless your methods, observations and the deductions from them are fully and accurately reported.

The record of your work must be made in the form of tables as follows:

SUBSTANCE C

Test	Method and observations	Inferences
(a) Potassium chromate solution		
(b) Dilute sulphuric acid		
(c) Mix hot, dilute solutions of C and D. Cool		
Further Tests (1) (2)		

SUBSTANCE D

Table as above

(L)

ACCOUNT OF LABORATORY WORK

DESCRIPTION OF SUBSTANCES

C : colourless, odourless, crystalline solid
D : colourless, odourless, crystalline solid

Lack of colour probably indicates absence of ions of all common transition metals except Zn^{2+}, Cd^{2+}, Hg^{2+}, Hg_2^{2+}, Ag^+.

Lack of smell would rule out ammonium salts of weak acids (e.g. $(NH_4)_2CO_3$, CH_3COONH_4)

PREPARATION OF SOLUTIONS

Solutions of C and D were prepared separately in distilled water as instructed – both dissolved easily in cold. Both solutions were colourless

Soluble salts of Sn^{2+}, Sn^{4+}, Hg_2^{2+}, Bi^{3+}, Sb^{3+} probably absent because these rarely dissolve easily in water unless acid is added to prevent hydrolysis

EFFECT OF SOLUTIONS ON LITMUS PAPER

Solution C : no effect on litmus paper

Solution D : blue litmus turned red

C is possibly the salt of a strong acid and a strong base – perhaps an alkali metal or an alkaline earth present with one of SO_4^{2-}, NO_3^- or halide – not SO_4^{2-} if alkaline earth

D is possibly the salt of a strong acid and a weak base. It could be an acid salt, though only one containing HSO_4^- or $H_2PO_4^-$ since these are the only acid anions which normally give an acid reaction with litmus in aqueous solution

TESTS ON SOLUTION OF SUBSTANCE C

Test	Method and Observations	Inferences
a) Potassium chromate solution	One drop of K_2CrO_4 aq was added to about 3 cm³ of test solution. An immediate pale yellow ppt was obtained. Addition of more reagent gave more ppt. The suspension was heated, gently at first, then almost to boiling — there was no observable change other than a tendency to increase particle size	Insoluble chromate pptd, possibly Ba^{2+} or Pb^{2+} present — more likely Ba^{2+} because of pale nature of ppt. No change on heating would indicate Ba^{2+} rather than Pb^{2+} because $PbCrO_4$ gives orange basic chromate when heated with water
b) Dilute sulphuric acid	One drop of dil.H_2SO_4 was added to about 3 cm³ of test solution. An immediate white ppt was obtained. Further addition of reagent produced more ppt. Heating the suspension had no effect on colour, solubility or smell, but particle size increased slightly and ppt settled more quickly	Insoluble sulphate pptd. Those likely under these conditions are $BaSO_4$, $CaSO_4$, $PbSO_4$, Hg_2SO_4, (possibly even Ag_2SO_4). Not Ca^{2+} because its chromate is soluble; Hg_2^{2+} is unlikely because (a) C dissolved readily in water and (b) mercury(I) chromate is orange-brown rather than yellow. Evidence so far indicates Ba^{2+} and C is probably the nitrate or a halide
c) Mix hot, dilute solution of C and D. Cool	Hot, almost boiling, 5 cm³ portions of solutions of C and D were mixed in a test-tube (it was considered that the solutions as prepared were 'dilute'). There was no immediately apparent effect. The mixed solution was cooled slightly under the tap and a white, sparkling, snow-like ppt began to form and settle out. The ppt became quite heavy on further cooling. The suspension was reheated and the ppt dissolved; on cooling again it re-appeared	D almost certainly not a sulphate because $BaSO_4$ (also $PbSO_4$) are insoluble, even in hot water. The mixed solution clearly contained Pb^{2+} ions and halide ions since, of common substances, only lead(II) halides show this marked solubility gradient with temperature. The ppt could not be PbI_2 because this is yellow

Test	Observation	Deduction
		The above evidence points to C being $BaCl_2$ or $BaBr_2$ and D being $Pb(NO_3)_2$ or $(CH_3COO)_2Pb$ (only two common, soluble salts of Pb) – but perhaps soln. D too acid to litmus to be $(CH_3COO)_2Pb$
Further test (1) Flame test	A little of solid C was placed on a nichrome wire (that had been moistened with conc. HCl) which was then held in a hot bunsen flame. An apple-green colour was imparted to the flame	Ba^{2+} confirmed. (Cu^{2+} also gives a green flame but this has a bluish appearance and, anyway, the colourless nature of C and the above reactions rule this out)
Further test (2) Silver nitrate	A few drops of silver nitrate solution were added to about 5 cm³ of solution C. A white, curdy ppt was obtained. The ppt rapidly dissolved on addition of ammonia solution. (A sodium carbonate extract was not prepared because Ba^{2+} does not interfere at either stage)	White ppt of AgCl rather than AgBr (which is pale cream) and also AgBr dissolves in bench ammonia only with difficulty. Dissolving of AgCl in ammonia solution is by formation of soluble complex containing $Ag(NH_3)_2^+$ ions

TESTS ON SOLUTION OF SUBSTANCE D

From test (c) on substance C above, it seems likely that substance D is either $Pb(NO_3)_2$ or $(CH_3COO)_2Pb$.

Test	Method and Observations	Inferences
(a) Potassium chromate solution	A drop of the reagent was added to about 3 cm^3 of soln. D — an immediate canary yellow ppt was obtained. Addition of more reagent gave more ppt. The suspension was warmed and then almost boiled and the ppt turned orange and became more granular	Insoluble chromate pptd, probably PbCrO$_4$ rather than BaCrO$_4$ because of intensity of colour. Change of colour almost certainly confirms Pb^{2+} — the orange colour indicating formation of basic lead(II) chromate
(b) Dilute sulphuric acid	One drop of dil.H$_2$SO$_4$ was added to about 3 cm^3 of test solution (D). An immediate white ppt was obtained. More reagent produced more ppt. The suspension was heated, gently at first, and then almost boiled. Heating had no effect on colour or smell but some increase in particle size was apparent	Insoluble sulphate pptd. In the light of test (a) and the tests on substance C, the ppt is probably PbSO$_4$. The lack of any smell of vinegar would rule out the presence of CH$_3$COO$^-$ and so D is probably Pb(NO$_3$)$_2$
(c) Mix hot, dilute solutions of C and D. Cool	Method and observation as in table above for substance C	As C was shown to contain Cl$^-$ ions, the white ppt obtained here is clearly PbCl$_2$
Further test (1) Potassium iodide solution	One drop of KI soln. was added to 2 or 3 cm^3 of solution C. An immediate canary yellow ppt was obtained	Yellow ppt would be PbI$_2$ — confirming the presence of Pb^{2+}
Further test (2) Heat on solid	A little of the solid C was heated in an ignition tube. A brown gas was evolved and there was a yellow residue on cooling	Brown gas (NO$_2$) confirms nitrate, and yellow residue (probably PbO) is further evidence in support of lead. The brown gas was not tested because it could not be Br$_2$ or CrO$_2$Cl$_2$